WHAT ON EARTH?

Rain Forest

BART AND LYNN KING

High Noon Books
Novato, California

Editor: Michael Milone
Interior Illustrations: Cynthia Coverston
Cover Design: Bonni Gatter

International Standard Book Number: 978-1-57128-505-8

18 17 16 15 14 13 12 11 10 09
10 09 08 07 06 05 04 03 02 01

You will enjoy all the High Noon Books.
Write for a free full list of titles or visit us at
www.HighNoonBooks.com.

Contents

CHAPTER 1

Warm and Wet

Nate stepped off the plane. He turned to face his three pals and read from a list. "Bug spray?" he asked.

"Got it!" said Tess.

"Sun screen?" Nate asked.

"Check!" said Sam.

"Cool clothes and hiking boots?" Nate asked.

"Yes, yes!" said Val.

They were spending a week in the rain

forest. And Nate was acting like he was in charge. The plan for this trip had started with him.

Nate had found out about a group of people. They worked to save the world's rain forests. Nate wanted to help them. He sent a gift of cash to the group. Then Nate began to get e-mails from the group. He learned about trips into the rain forest. He told his pals about the trips. They all wanted to go. But there were things that had to be worked out first.

"You want to go where?" Val's dad asked.

"How much will it cost?" Sam's mom and dad asked.

"Can I come, too?" Tess's mom asked.

"We'll think about it," said Nate's folks.

The four pals wrote to the rain forest group. They told the group about the films they made. A film on the rain forest could help the group to reach its goals. It could be a great teaching tool. It could help the group to raise cash. They could buy more land to save. At the end of the note, Nate, Sam, Tess, and Val asked for something big. "Would you trade the cost of our trip for a film on the rain forest?"

The group said yes to the trade. And now the four friends were in the rain forest. Close to it, anyway. A man named Ray met them at the airport. He took them to a small boat in the town. They climbed on board and sat down. Ray steered the boat up a stream. The town slipped away behind them. The green of the rain forest pulled them in.

The air was warm, about 80 degrees. The four friends were used to the heat. Back home, it could get very hot. But at home it was a dry kind of heat. Here, the warm air seemed thick and wet. They soon began to sweat.

"It is not even raining," said Sam. "I am soaked."

Ray laughed. He told Sam to wait for a while. There would be rain before they got to the lodge.

"Rain forests like this are warm places. It stays warm all year. It can rain all year. There are no cold or dry spells. We get at least four inches of rain a month here," said Ray. "But sometimes we get up to six inches in one day!"

Val leaned back. She was tired but did not dare close her eyes. Huge bugs with blue wings zoomed past. Birds screeched down from the sky. Nate stared at the huge trees. They grew along the banks of the stream. Their roots were twisted and thick. Sam peered down into the water. What fish and snakes lived there? There was too much mud in the water to tell. Tess took a deep breath. The rain forest air smelled dark and rich.

An hour later, Ray steered the boat to a small dock. "Here we are," he said. "Home, sweet home." Just then, it started to rain. Ray led them to the main lodge. It was a large space made out of palm trees. It had a leaf roof. The floor was raised off the ground. There were no walls. The four pals signed in. They found out which huts they would be staying in.

"Get a good night's sleep," Ray said. "And be sure to use your nets!" Then he headed off to his own hut.

Ray led them to the main lodge. It was a large
space made out of palm trees.

CHAPTER 2

Pigs and Palms

Sam's skin was puffed up the next day. Every part of him itched. He scratched and scratched. That made him feel worse. Sam had not used the net that was around his bed. The bugs had bothered him all night long. He had bug bites from head to toe.

Ray shook his head when he saw Sam. "About 6,000," he said. When the pals gave Ray an odd look, he went on. "That is how many bugs live in this little slice of rain forest. And it looks like they all found Sam!"

Ray would be spending the day with the four friends. "This rain forest is a kind of park," he said. "This means that this rain forest is now safe. It will be kept as a wild place. It can not be turned into land for farming or for homes. It is no longer OK to log or hunt here. The plants, the animals, and the land are safe. The forest will be here to enjoy and to study."

Ray led them on a path as he talked. He said that keeping the rain forest park safe was a good first step. But more had to be done. The park was a small piece of land for so many living things. It was too small for the large animals. They needed room to roam.

"Do you mean like big cats?" asked Tess.

Ray nodded. "Cats, deer, monkeys, and pigs need room, too. The pigs root around at night," he said. "They dig through the rain forest floor with their long snouts. They are looking for food. They help to break up the soil." Ray talked about how the pigs ate many things. They liked roots, leaves, grubs, and worms. Some even ate mice and frogs. Ray pointed out a spot on the rain forest floor. Some pigs had been there the night before.

"Hey!" said Sam. Something soft had dropped on his head. It looked kind of like a plum.

Ray laughed. "That is a sweet fig," he said.

"Pigs love figs."

Nate thought about what Ray said about the lack of space. "What can we do?" he asked. "Will the large animals be able to live? We can't just plant a few new trees and call it a rain forest. Places like this take more than 2,000 years to grow!"

"You are right," said Ray. "But here is some good news. We are making a path. The path will be a kind of highway for animals. It will join this rain forest park to another one not far from here. This will give the animals twice as much space."

Rain forests once made up 1/7 of Earth's land. But the last 100 years have been hard. The world's rain forests are changing. The change is not good. Rain forests are getting smaller each year. Nate, Tess, Val, and Sam were worried. They wanted to help. "Show us all that you can," they said to Ray. And he did. The four pals made videos of everything.

The "hot lips" plant was a big hit. This is a plant that grows on the forest floor. Its bloom looks like a pair of bright pink lips. Ray then told them about a very odd plant. It grew in another rain forest. This plant seemed to have no roots, no stem, and no leaves. But its bloom was three feet wide! Flies loved the huge bloom. It smelled like rotting meat. "Yuck!" said Val, making a face.

All day, they hiked through the trees. Many of the trees Ray showed them were palms. He said there were 3,000 kinds of palms. Most of them had tall, smooth trunks. They were just as thick up high as they were down low. The leaves of the palm grew out of its top. They looked like a big green crown. Some palms had leaves that were 30 feet long!

On one trunk, Nate saw something odd. It looked like a bunch of sharp thorns. "Those are tree hoppers," Ray said. "They are a kind of bug. Many rain forest animals eat bugs. Looking like thorns helps keep the bugs safe." Ray told Nate and his pals to take a close look. And sure thing, those bright red thorns had legs!

CHAPTER 3

Rain Forest Ropes

"Can we change huts?" Nate asked his pals. Nate's eyes were red. He had not slept a wink. Sam had talked in his sleep all night long. "What were you dreaming about, anyway?" he asked Sam.

Sam shrugged. He was not sure. "I'll let you know if it comes to me," he said.

Just then Ray showed up. He was with a woman. Her name was Brit. She had a large pack on her back. "Come on," she said. "We have a full day planned."

Brit and Ray led the four pals on a short hike. Brit was at the front, and Ray at the back. Sometimes, Brit would stop and stare up into the trees. Then she would shake her head and move on. At last, she looked up and nodded. "This is it," she said. Brit took off her pack and pulled out gear. First, she took out six hard hats. "Put these on," she said.

Next, Brit took out a large hunting bow. Nate, Sam, Val, and Tess were shocked. They thought that hunting in this rain forest had been stopped. Ray told them that Brit used her bow for something else. She used it to shoot ropes and nets up into the trees. They would climb the ropes and nets. Then they could take a look around. "The best way to see a rain forest is from up high!" said Brit.

The four pals learned as they climbed. "Trees are a key part of the rain forest," said Ray. "They help life on Earth in many ways. Trees are a place for animals to live. They are food for animals to eat. They help to keep the water in rivers clean. They keep the soil in place when it rains."

"The rain forest is one big place," said Brit. "But it has zones. These are different parts." As they went up, they saw what Brit meant. The rain forest changed. The first zone was the forest floor. The ground was soft with old

"The best way to see a rain forest is from up high," said Brit.

leaves, moss, logs, and blooms. Huge King ferns with fat leaves reached up from the ground. There they saw tall, flat tree roots. The roots rose out of the ground like walls. They held the tallest trees of the rain forest in place. Ferns, vines, and flowers grew on the trunks of the trees. Some of the trees were hard to see because of all the plants growing on them.

Brit stopped and sat on a branch. She talked about some things they saw. Ants marched past. They carried leaves and dead bugs. Birds flew all around. They screamed and screeched. "Most of the birds nest in the next zone up," said Brit. "But they come down here to feed. The birds eat bugs, seeds, and figs."

Nate, Val, Sam, and Tess looked around. It was brighter here. Trees and plants need sunlight to make food. The leaves on the trees up high were small. Their color was light green. Down below it was less bright. The leaves on the plants were big and dark. The big leaves on the plants down low helped the plants to catch sunlight.

Brit said they were just under a place called the crown. The crown was the top of the rain forest. A few very tall trees poked up past the crown. They were the trees with the huge roots.

Tess felt something crawl on her hand. "Oh, look!" she said. "A small crab!" Tess held still. She did not want to scare the crab.

Sam leaned in close to take a look. "Hey, Nate," he said. "I thought you were the only crab on this trip."

"That's it," said Nate. "I'm changing huts."

"There are lots of crabs in the rain forest," said Brit with a laugh. "Some live way up here in little pools." She pointed to some leaves filled with water. "And some live down there," she said, pointing to the forest floor.

"The ones down there are like the pigs I told you about," added Ray. "They eat the stuff on the forest floor."

They left Brit to do some of her work up in the trees. On the ground, Ray showed them something else. It was an earthworm. The worm helped to keep the forest floor clean. The pals

had never seen a worm like this. It was six feet

long. The worm was as thick as Ray's thumb!

CHAPTER 4

Night Notes

The pals left Brit in the afternoon. Ray told the four friends to get some rest. He said he had big plans for that night. A break sounded good to them. Val would draw some of the plants and animals she had seen. Tess would read about the park. Sam would find a snack at the lodge. And Nate would try to get some sleep.

Now it was dark. The moon was up. The rain forest was thick with plants. Only a little light got to the forest floor. Nate, Sam, Tess, and Val met at the start of the trail. They were waiting for Ray. The air was filled with sound. Tree frogs and water frogs croaked like mad. Bugs chirped and clicked. Birds called out and sang. Deep in the forest, pigs grunted.

At last, Ray showed up. "Here," he said. He gave each of them a flashlight. "Turn these on only if you have to," he said. "You will see more without them." Ray told them they were in for a treat. The moon was bright that night. It was a great time to see the night life in a rain forest.

Ray led them to a bend in the trail. He stopped and faced the four of them. Ray pointed to his nose. He wanted them to smell something.

Nate, Tess, Sam, and Val each took a deep breath. What was that smell? It was sweet but strong. Then they saw a tree trunk near them. It had big white flowers all over it. Some of their roots clung to the tree. Some of the roots hung like threads in the air. But here was the odd thing. They had passed this tree before, in the daylight. There had been no smell then. There had been no blooms.

Ray spoke in a low tone. He said that some plants bloom just at night. Bugs come to the strong smell of the blooms. The bugs went inside the blooms to feed. When the bugs come out, they have bloom dust on them. Then the bugs go to another plant to feed some more.

Some of the dust stays on the other plant. The dust helps the plants make seeds. The bugs were like little farmers. They helped plants spread from place to place.

Just then a huge moth flew past. The moth was a pale white. It landed on one of the blooms and began to feed. "With the moonlight, I think we can get this on film," said Val, looking through the lens. The moth was almost the same white as the flowers.

From there, Ray led them to a new spot. "Wow!" said Sam under his breath. The air was filled with little sparks. The sparks moved! Ray pointed down. Rain had pooled on the ground. It made a kind of swamp. Then he pointed to his ear. They heard it. The air hummed with the sound of bugs. The flying sparks were fire-flies! Ray told them that the bugs used light to find their mates. The four pals felt like they were dreaming. This rain forest scene seemed too cool to be real.

Ray hoped to show them a masked owl or a great horned owl. Owls are night birds. They have good eyes and strong claws. They are good hunters. Owls eat moths, frogs, snakes, and mice. Sometimes they even catch fish! But not one owl was seen.

They all started back. Ray stopped once more. "Hold very still," he said. "Now look to my right." The four pals looked that way. All they saw was the dark outline of a tree. It had no blooms. There were no sparks. "Keep your eyes on that low branch," said Ray. As they watched, something moved. It had four legs and a head. It was hanging upside down. The thing was a sloth!

It had four legs and a head. It was hanging
upside down. The thing was a sloth!

CHAPTER 5

Stream Sights

It was the next morning. Ray was taking the four pals to the next rain forest park. A new path would soon join the two parks. Animals could walk from one park to the other. For now, going by boat was the best way to get there.

"The sloth had such long hair!" said Nate.

"And it moved so slowly," said Sam. "Now I know why my dad sometimes calls me a sloth."

In the back of the boat, Ray laughed. He

steered around a turn in the stream. "Sloths can take a whole hour to go just 12 feet. They move so slowly that moss grows on them!"

The day was warm. Nate and Sam wanted to go for a swim. They knew this was not a safe place. "Is it true that there are fish with sharp teeth that can tear someone to shreds?" Nate asked. Ray made a face. He said it was rare for fish to do this. He said one kind of fish has sharp teeth. The fish might attack an animal or human if there is blood in the water. If they smell it, watch out. They strike fast.

There was a great view from the boat. Up close, it was hard to see into the rain forest. It had too many plants. But from the water, the view was better. You could see how the forest rose hundreds of feet into the bright blue sky.

Ray turned the motor off. He let the boat drift to one side of the stream. The water was calm there. Flat round leaves floated all around them. The leaves were huge. Some were as big as a child's wading pool. Ray said the leaves could grow to be seven feet across. A pale pink bloom grew from a stem on each leaf. The friends could not see the roots. Ray said they reach all the way down to the mud. When the water rises, the stems grow. They could grow up to eight inches a day.

Birds nested on some of the big green pads. Frogs jumped from one pad to the next. Tess made sure to catch the pretty scene on film. They were about to leave when Sam blurted out something.

"Snakes!" he said.

CHAPTER 6

So Many Snakes

"Snakes," said Sam again. "That's what I was dreaming about two nights ago."

Sam's pals sighed. Sam had not seen any snakes. He had only dreamed about them! They joked and said they wanted to toss Sam from the boat. Ray just smiled. He asked what kind of snakes were in Sam's dream.

"Big ones," said Sam.

Ray said that the rain forest had lots of snakes. Some were big and others were small.

33

"One of these is the boa," he said. A sand boa is only three feet long. But the green boa is 30 feet long. It can weigh more than 400 pounds. The boa hunted at night. It had a nose with tiny parts called cells. The cells could feel heat. Some animals gave off heat. When one came close to the snake, the boa could feel the heat. The snake knew it was time to strike.

Ray had more to tell about snakes. Lots of rain forest snakes lived in the water. A snake could pump itself with air. This helped the snake to float. When the snake wanted to dive, it let some of the air out.

Some snakes lived in the water and on land. The king cobra was one of these. Nate,

Tess, Sam, and Val knew what a cobra looked like. This snake could raise its head off the ground. The skin around the snake's head opened wide. It looked a little like a hood. This helped the snake look bigger.

Snakes lived in the trees, too. Some of them look just like vines. Blending in is the key to staying safe in the rain forest. Birds and frogs came near them. They might even land on a snake. Then, gulp, they were the snake's next meal!

Nate stared into the water. "What about eels?" he asked. "Are eels just water snakes?"

"No," said Ray. "Eels look and move a little like snakes. But they are a kind of fish."

Snakes lived in the trees, too. Some of them look just like vines.

There are about 600 kinds of eels in the world. Most of them live in the ocean. Some live in fresh water. Eels like streams with a mud bottom. The eels that live in this stream are a green-brown color. They grow to eight feet long. Some can weigh about 100 pounds. They use a kind of shock to kill or stun their prey. The shock is like a strong sting.

Val sat at the front of the boat. "Snakes and eels, snakes and eels," she said. "Let's talk about something cool, like bugs!" Val was a big bug fan. If she saw a new one, she grabbed her sketch book and started to draw.

"You may be the next Lucy Cheesman," said Ray. He told them about Lucy. She was born in England in the late 1800s. She grew up loving animals of all kinds, not just bugs. Lucy wanted to be a vet – an animal doctor. In those days, girls could not go to vet school. They could study bugs. So Lucy learned all she could about bugs. Later, a zoo near her home hired her. She was the first woman to work at the zoo.

"She should have come to the rain forest," said Val.

"She did," said Ray with a smile. "Lucy ended up spending 12 years going to the world's rain forests. She even got a bug named after her!"

CHAPTER 7

Rain Forest Foods

It was time to leave the rain forest. Tess, Val, Sam, and Nate packed their things. They swept their huts. The four of them walked the path to the lodge one last time. They were going to miss this green place.

Ray and Brit waited for them under the palm leaf roof. They had a big tray filled with snacks. Sam's eyes lit up. He was always in the mood for a snack. There were fruit and nuts. There was a big bowl of rice and some jars of spice. There were candy bars, corn chips, and pop to drink. It seemed like an odd mix of things. But the pals did not say anything. They did not want to be rude.

"All of these foods are the same in some way," said Brit. "Do you know how?"

Sam, Tess, Val, and Nate took a close look at the snacks on the tray. Were they all health foods? No. Were they all sweet foods? No. Did all of these foods grow on trees? No.

"These foods all come from the rain forest," said Ray.

Val shook her head. "That can't be," she said. "Sure, fruit and nuts grow here. We saw them in the trees. But corn chips? Pop? Candy?"

"The corn in corn chips first came from the rain forest," said Brit. "This kind of soda is made from a nut. It is called a cola nut."

"What about the candy bars?" asked Sam. "If those grow on trees, it will make my day."

"They don't grow on trees," said Brit. "But they are made from a bean that does. It grows in pods on a tree."

Ray said that other foods came from here, too. And food was not the only thing folks needed from the rain forest. The trees and plants there helped to clean the air. They cooled Earth. Their roots held the soil in place. Trees were both food and home to all kinds of life.

"We now see why saving rain forest land is

such a big deal," said Val. "Without places like this, life on Earth will change. It might not be a good change."

"Yes," said Nate. He was pleased the trip had gone so well. "And we hope our film helps to spread the word."